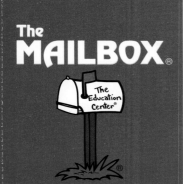
The **MAILBOX**®
The Education Center®

LET'S DO

Science
Today!

Step-by-step investigations that build scientific method skills.

S0-AFN-380

- ✳ **Observing**
- ✳ **Describing**
- ✳ **Discussing**
- ✳ **Predicting**

- ✳ **Asking questions**
- ✳ **Comparing**
- ✳ **Connecting**

and more!

Plus follow-up activities and reproducibles!

Managing Editor: Kimberly Brugger-Murphy

Editorial Team: Becky S. Andrews, Diane Badden, Kimberley Bruck, Karen A. Brudnak, Kitty Campbell, Pam Crane, Chris Curry, Lynette Dickerson, Tazmen Hansen, Marsha Heim, Lori Z. Henry, Debra Liverman, Dorothy C. McKinney, Thad H. McLaurin, Brenda Miner, Suzanne Moore, Sharon Murphy, Jennifer Nunn, Gerri Primak, Mark Rainey, Greg D. Rieves, Hope Rodgers, Leanne Stratton Swinson, Zane Williard

www.themailbox.com

Table of Contents

What's Inside

Easy to Plan and Prepare

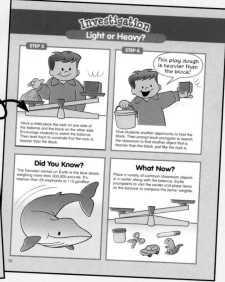

Take the steps with you! Simply tear out the page and slip it inside a plastic page protector!

Easy to Lead

Easy to Carry Out and Extend

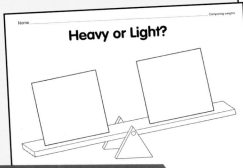

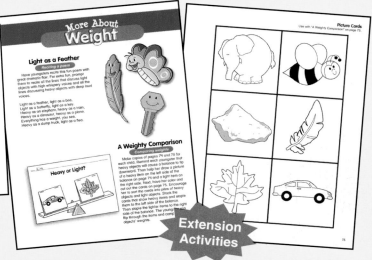

Extension Activities

Key Science Learning
The sense of touch is more sensitive in some parts of the body than others.

During the investigation, students

- make observations
- use their sense of touch to gather information
- make comparisons
- discuss and draw conclusions

Materials:
piece of plastic canvas
piece of bubble wrap
craft feather
kitchen scrubber

Getting Started
Ask children to touch a variety of objects and describe how they feel.

Investigation
Sense of Touch

I feel things with my fingers.

Invite a small group of youngsters to join you at a table. Have students examine their fingers. Then ask, "How do you use your fingers?" Lead students to conclude that fingers help them feel and grasp objects.

It feels soft and fluffy. It's hard in the middle.

Display the materials. Then instruct students to use their fingertips to examine the feather. Ask, "How does the feather feel?"

?

Have each child touch one of her elbows. Ask, "Do you think the feather will feel the same when you touch it with your elbow?"

The feather feels soft, but I don't feel the hard part!

Have each child rub the feather on her elbow and describe what she feels.

STEP 5

Have students repeat Steps 2 through 4 with each remaining item, guiding students to realize that fingertips are better at feeling details than elbows.

STEP 6

I can feel more with my fingertips!

Lead students to conclude that certain parts of the body are more sensitive to touch than others. Thus the more sensitive parts are able to feel things with greater detail.

This Is Why

The tiny nerves that supply the sense of touch are not spread out evenly over the body, but are grouped in clusters. The feeling of pressure is greatest where there are the most tiny nerves. The fingertips, the tongue, and the tip of the nose have the largest number of tiny nerves, making them the most sensitive parts of the body.

What Now?

Have students experiment with other items, such as a fuzzy blanket, an ice cube, and a pinecone. Encourage them to touch each object to the tips of their noses, their knees, and the bottoms of their feet. Have students describe how each object feels. Then help little ones use their new knowledge to discuss the sense of touch.

More About
The Sense of Touch

When I Touch
Singing a song

Have little ones sing this song to reinforce information about the sense of touch.

(sung to the tune of "Where Is Thumbkin?")

When I touch,
When I touch,
I can feel,
I can feel,
Whether something's bumpy,
Hard, soft, or lumpy;
Cold as ice;
Warm and nice.

It's a Mystery!
Developing the sense of touch

Engage youngsters' critical-thinking skills when they play this game! Gather a few familiar items, along with a blindfold. Invite a volunteer to put the blindfold on. Then hand her one of the objects. Have her feel the object, describe what she feels, and then guess what the object is. Finally, have her remove the blindfold to confirm the identity of the object. Continue in the same manner with new volunteers.

Sense of Touch Expert

_____
Name

Ask me about
the sense of touch!

Sense of Touch Expert

_____
Name

Ask me about
the sense of touch!

Sense of Touch Expert

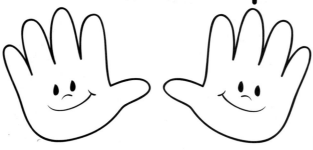

_____
Name

Ask me about
the sense of touch!

Sense of Touch Expert

_____
Name

Ask me about
the sense of touch!

Let's Do Science Today! • ©The Mailbox® Books • TEC61164

8   **Brag Tags:** Copy the notes onto colorful paper and use as desired.

How Do They Feel?

Note to the teacher: Have the child name each picture and describe how the object would feel. Then have him color the pictures.

Key Science Learning
The brain can distinguish between a variety of smells.

During the investigation, students

- make observations
- use their sense of smell to gather information
- make comparisons
- identify and match scents

Materials:
6 small containers with lids
6 cotton balls, dampened with fabric softener, pickle juice, and vinegar to make matching pairs

In advance, place each cotton ball in a separate container. Then secure each lid.

Getting Started
Have students name something that smells good and something that smells bad.

STEP 1

Gather a small group of youngsters at a table. Ask, "What does your nose do?" After students explain that a nose smells things, tell them that the smell of something is called its scent. Have students tell about a scent they have experienced.

STEP 2

Display the containers holding the dampened cotton balls. Remove the lid from one container and demonstrate how to wave it under your nose to smell the scent.

STEP 3

Have each child smell the cotton ball in the container. Ask, "What does the smell make you think of?"

STEP 4

Remove the lid from a second container and, once again, have each student smell the cotton ball. Ask, "Does this scent smell the same as the other scent?" If the scents match, a student moves both containers to the side. If not, the process is repeated with the remaining containers until a match is found.

STEP 5

Both of these smell like pickles!

Have students repeat Steps 3 and 4 with the remaining containers.

STEP 6

Lead students to conclude that their noses can smell many different scents and help them gather information from their surroundings.

This Is Why

Odors come from tiny bits of gas released into the air by different substances. The gases stimulate receptor cells inside the nose, and then the receptor cells send messages to a part of the brain called the *olfactory bulb*. The brain is then able to determine what the smell is.

What Now?

Have students go on a scent hunt! Place one half of an orange in a paper bag and hide the remaining half somewhere in the room. Encourage each child to sniff the contents of the bag and then walk around the room sniffing the air to find the matching scent.

The Sense of Smell

Block That Smell!

Observation skills

This activity shows students that taste and smell work together. Gather a variety of foods, along with a pitcher of water and cups. Invite each child to taste a food while holding his nose closed to block the smell. Have him drink some water, and then taste the same food again without holding his nose closed. Have the student describe which sample tasted better. Then explain to students that blocking the smell of food dulls its taste.

How Does It Smell?

🙂 Good	☹ Bad	😐 No Smell
Cinnamon		comb

How Does It Smell?

Classifying smells

Cut out a copy of the cards on page 14 and obtain the item shown on each card. Also make a chart similar to the one shown. Display the items. To begin, invite a student to choose an item and smell it. Ask if she thinks the item smells good, bad, or has no smell at all. Then have her place the corresponding picture card in the appropriate column on the chart. Continue in the same manner with the remaining items.

Picture Cards

Use with "How Does It Smell?" on page 13.

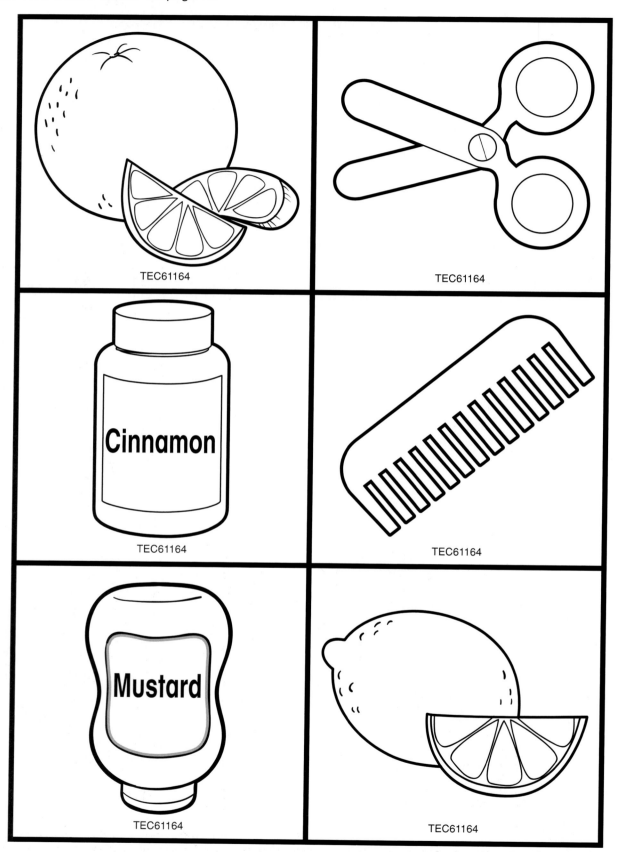

TEC61164

TEC61164

Cinnamon

TEC61164

TEC61164

Mustard

TEC61164

TEC61164

Let's Do Science Today! • ©The Mailbox® Books • TEC61164

I can smell…

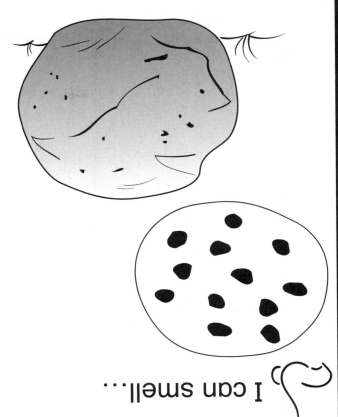

I can smell…

I can smell…

I Can
Smell...

Name _____

Let's Do Science Today! • ©The Mailbox® Books • TEC61164

Fold-and-Go Booklet: To make a booklet, cut on the bold line. Fold along the thin horizontal line (keeping the programming to the outside) and then fold along the thin vertical line (keeping the cover to the outside). Have each child circle or color on each page the picture of the object with a scent.

Key Science Learning
A sound originates with the vibration of an object.

During the investigation, students

- listen
- follow directions
- make observations
- make predictions

Materials:
shallow pan of water
triangle and mallet

Getting Started
Ask youngsters which parts of their bodies they use to hear.

Good Vibrations

STEP 1

Gather a small group of children and present the triangle. Allow each child to touch and explore the triangle.

STEP 2

CLINK!

Hold the triangle by the metal (as opposed to the hanger) and allow each child to tap it with the mallet. Encourage students to describe the sound it makes. Ask, "Is there a better way to hold the triangle?"

STEP 3

The sound lasts longer!

Next, hold the triangle by the hanger and encourage each student to tap it with the mallet. Once again, have students describe the sound. Explain to students that the triangle vibrates, or moves back and forth very quickly, when tapped and this vibration leads to a sound. When the metal of the triangle was held, the triangle wasn't allowed to vibrate as much.

STEP 4

The water will splash all over!

Tell students that you are going to place part of the triangle in the water. Have students predict what will happen if they strike the triangle while it is in the water.

Investigation
Good Vibrations

STEP 5

There are little waves!

Place the triangle in the water and then encourage a child to gently strike the triangle with the mallet. Ask, "What do you see?"

STEP 6

Remind students that hitting the triangle with the mallet causes the triangle to vibrate. This movement causes the little waves in the water.

Did You Know?

The muscles that connect the outer ear to the head have no actual use, but some people can move them and thus can wiggle their ears! Many animals, such as rabbits, have highly movable ears.

What Now?

Invite students to experiment with other items—such as a hand drum, a tambourine, or their own vocal chords—to see how they vibrate and make sounds!

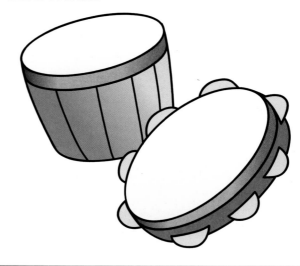

The Mystery Sound

Developing critical listening skills

Gather two identical sets of rhythm instruments. Place one set in plain sight and conceal the other set from youngsters' view. As students listen closely, play each visible instrument and review the instrument's name. Next, play one of the concealed instruments. Then have students guess which instrument made the sound. Continue in the same way with each remaining instrument.

I hear the tambourine!

HELLO, CLASS!

Who Was That?

Speaking to play a game

Record each child saying, "Hello, class!" on an audiotape. (Make sure you write a list of youngsters' names in the order their voices are recorded.) Gather youngsters in your large-group area. Then play one of the recordings. Invite students to guess the classmate that recorded the words. Then repeat the process for each voice on the cassette. What fun!

What Makes Noise?

 Circle.

Today we did an experiment on sound.

Ask me about it!

Let's Do Science Today! • ©The Mailbox® Books • TEC61164

Today we did an experiment on sound.

Ask me about it!

Let's Do Science Today! • ©The Mailbox® Books • TEC61164

Today we did an experiment on sound.

Ask me about it!

Let's Do Science Today! • ©The Mailbox® Books • TEC61164

Today we did an experiment on sound.

Ask me about it!

Let's Do Science Today! • ©The Mailbox® Books • TEC61164

Key Science Learning
People use the five senses to gather information about the world.

During the investigation, students

- follow directions
- make observations
- describe using all five senses
- draw conclusions

Materials:
box of crisp rice cereal
milk
bowl (for each child)
spoon (for each child)
5-column chart, each
    column labeled with a
    different sense
marker

Getting Started
Help students identify
the five senses.

Investigation
The Five Senses

STEP 1

Gather a small group of youngsters at a table. Have each student examine the unopened box of cereal. Ask, "Can you tell me something about what is inside the box?"

STEP 2

Open the box and help each youngster pour a small amount of cereal into his bowl. Encourage students to describe the cereal using color, size, shape, and texture words. Write student responses in the "Sight" column on the chart.

STEP 3

Invite each child to smell the cereal and then describe the cereal's scent. Record youngsters' responses.

STEP 4

Instruct each child to listen carefully as you help her pour milk on her cereal. Then encourage her to describe any sounds she hears. Write students' words on the chart.

STEP 5

MMMM!

Invite each student to eat her cereal. Then encourage youngsters to describe the taste and texture. Record youngsters' responses on the chart. As the cereal absorbs the milk, ask, "Does the cereal feel different in your mouth than it did before?"

STEP 6

Five Senses Award
Presented to
Juliana
name
for participating in our five senses investigation.

Review the completed chart, leading students to conclude that the information listed on the chart was gathered through the use of their five senses. Then give each child a personalized copy of the five senses award on page 26.

Did You Know?

Our senses of hearing, sight, smell, taste, and touch are called our *external senses.* These senses send information to our brains from the outside environment. We also have *internal senses* that send messages to our brains about changes taking place inside the body, such as hunger, thirst, tiredness, or pain.

PUFFED CORN CEREAL

What Now?

Place an opened bag of flavored, rippled potato chips inside a grocery bag. Have each child close her eyes as she smells the chips. Invite her to describe the smell and guess the identity of the mystery food. Then give each child a chip. Have her examine the chip and feel its ridges. Then have her eat the chip, describing its texture, taste, and sound.

Our Five Senses

Recognizing the five senses

Have little ones sing this song to reinforce the concept that our five senses give us information about the world.

(sung to the tune of "Are You Sleeping?")

Seeing, smelling,
Tasting, touching,
Hearing too, will help you
Learn about your world,
Learn about your world.
Five senses, five senses.

Five Senses Toss

Identifying the five senses

Enlarge the patterns on page 27 and then color and cut out a copy of each. Attach the cutouts to a sheet of poster board and label them as shown to create a gameboard. To play, give a child a beanbag and have her toss it onto the gameboard. Have her identify the sense the beanbag landed on or near and then name something she can do with that sense. For example, if the beanbag lands on the ears, she might say she can hear her mom when she sings.

smell   touch   taste   hearing   sight

Five Senses Award

Presented to

_____
name

for participating in our five senses investigation.

TEC61164

Five Senses Award

Presented to

_____
name

for participating in our five senses investigation.

TEC61164

Let's Do Science Today! • ©The Mailbox® Books • TEC61164

26   **Note to the teacher:** Use with "The Five Senses" on pages 22–24.

TEC61164

TEC61164

TEC61164

TEC61164

TEC61164

Key Science Learning

Living things have specific needs.

During the investigation, students

- make observations
- describe the needs of living things
- compare living and nonliving things
- sort and classify

Materials:
photograph of an animal
rock
doll
2-column chart labeled
    "Living" and "Nonliving"
copy of the picture cards
    on page 32

Getting Started
Help students name some characteristics of living and nonliving things.

STEP 1

Invite a small group of students to join you at a table. Show youngsters the animal photograph and the rock. Ask, "Which object is alive and which is not alive? How do you know?"

STEP 2

Ask, "Are you alive?" Encourage students to explain their thoughts. Then have them name things they do that show they are living things. Invite youngsters to demonstrate if desired.

STEP 3

Have students compare themselves to adults. Ask, "What happens as you get older?" Lead students to conclude that as they get older they grow and change, which is a characteristic of a living thing. Then ask youngsters to name other things that grow and change.

STEP 4

Display the doll. Ask, "Can the doll do the things that you can do?" Have students describe the similarities and differences between themselves and the doll. Then ask, "Can the doll grow and change?" Lead youngsters to conclude that the doll looks like a person but is not alive because it does not have the characteristics of a living thing.

Investigation
Living and Nonliving

Have students name things they need to live and grow. Lead youngsters to conclude that all living things—such as people, animals, and plants—need food, water, and air to live and grow. Items that are not alive do not need these things.

Give students the set of picture cards from page 32. Have youngsters sort the cards onto the corresponding columns on the chart and explain why they think the objects pictured are living or nonliving things.

Did You Know?

Everything can be classified as living or nonliving. All types of living things eat, drink, digest, create waste, move, grow, reproduce, and breathe. A nonliving thing, such as fire, may have characteristics of a living thing because it can grow and move, but if it does not have all the characteristics, it cannot be called living.

What Now?

Tell students that you are thinking of something that is alive, is small, flies around flowers, and makes a buzzing sound. After students guess that the living object is a bee, repeat the activity, describing something that is nonliving. Continue with a variety of other objects.

More About
Living and Nonliving

Scouting the Outdoors
Sorting

Take students on an outdoor scavenger hunt! Divide a piece of paper in two and label the columns "Living" and "Nonliving." Place the paper on a clipboard. Take students outside to look for items that are living and items that are nonliving. Encourage youngsters to look up in the air and on the ground. Have students identify different items and tell you whether they are living or nonliving and explain why. After confirming each answer, write the name of the item in the appropriate column. When you return to the classroom, review the information on the chart with your students.

Living	Nonliving
ladybug	rocks
trees	house
cat	wall
bird	sticks
flowers	car
grass	
butterfly	
people	

A ___squirrel___ is ___living___

because it ___eats food___.

Class Book
Dictating information

Reinforce students' understanding of living and nonliving things with this idea! Help a youngster name something that is living or nonliving. Write its name in the first blank on a copy of page 33. Then help her dictate a response to complete the sentence. Encourage her to draw a picture that corresponds to the text. Bind the completed pages behind a cover and place the book in your reading area.

Picture Cards

Use with "Living and Nonliving" on pages 28–30.

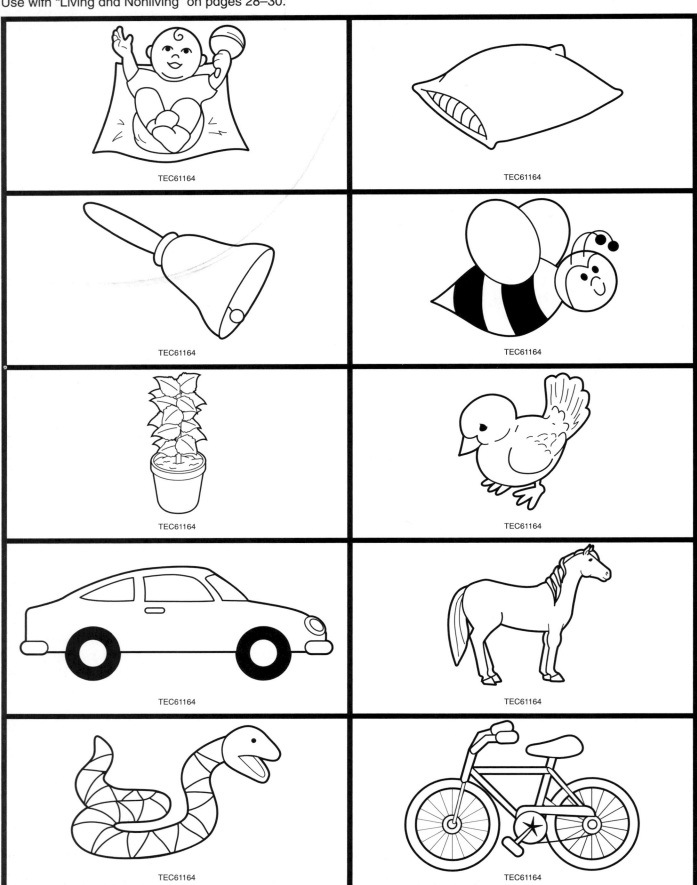

TEC61164

TEC61164

TEC61164

TEC61164

TEC61164

TEC61164

TEC61164

TEC61164

TEC61164

TEC61164

Let's Do Science Today! • ©The Mailbox® Books • TEC61164

A _____ is _____

because it _____.

Key Science Learning

Plants need water, sunlight, and soil to live and grow.

During the investigation, students

- make observations
- describe the conditions of the plants
- make comparisons
- discuss and draw conclusions

Materials:
2 potted plants
   (1 healthy, 1 wilting)
cup for each child
straw for each child
watering can and water

Getting Started

Ask students what they know about taking care of plants.

STEP 1

Gather a small group of students at a table and ask, "How do you feel when you get really thirsty?"

STEP 2

Display the wilting plant. Tell students that the plant has been neglected and has not received the proper amount of water and sunlight that it needs. Then have youngsters describe how the plant looks.

STEP 3

Have students gently feel the leaves and the soil and then describe what each feels like. Ask, "Do you think plants get thirsty too?" Encourage youngsters to use their observations of the plant to explain their reasoning.

STEP 4

Give each student a cup of water and invite him to drink it using a straw. Lead youngsters to conclude that they could drink the water because they have a mouth. Ask, "How do you think a plant drinks water, since it doesn't have a mouth?"

STEP 5

Have a volunteer water the wilting plant. Instruct students to watch as the soil absorbs the water. Explain that the soil holds the water and then the roots of the plant drink the water, similar to drinking through the straw, and send it up to the rest of the plant.

STEP 6

Display the healthy plant. Have students describe how it looks and how the leaves and soil feel. Ask youngsters to describe the similarities and differences between the plants. Lead students to conclude that plants are living things that need water, soil, and sunlight.

Did You Know?

Giant sequoias are the largest living trees in the world. A giant sequoia can grow up to 250 feet tall and over 30 feet wide, and it needs to drink thousands of gallons of water every day!

What Now?

Ask students what they think they could do to make the wilting plant healthy. Help them carefully remove any dead foliage from the plant. Have a volunteer water the plant and then place the plant near a window. Assign a different child each day to help take care of the plant. No matter what the outcome, this extension will reinforce the importance of taking care of a plant's basic needs.

More About Plant Needs

Sun, Water, Soil
Identifying a plant's needs

When students sing this song, it reinforces their understanding of what plants need to live and grow.

(sung to the tune of "Mary Had a Little Lamb")

Plants need sunlight, water, and soil;
Water and soil; water and soil.
Plants need sunlight, water, and soil
To help them live and grow.

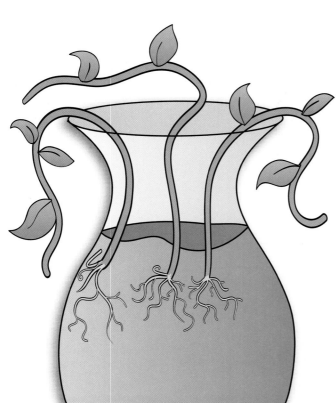

Growing Roots
Investigating living things

Students will observe how roots grow with this activity! Take several clippings from household plants and place them in a clear container with water. Mark a calendar to show the date. Have youngsters observe the clippings each day. Mark the calendar again when the first root is observed, and then help youngsters determine how many days it took for the root to grow. After all of the stems have developed several roots, plant them in a container of soil.

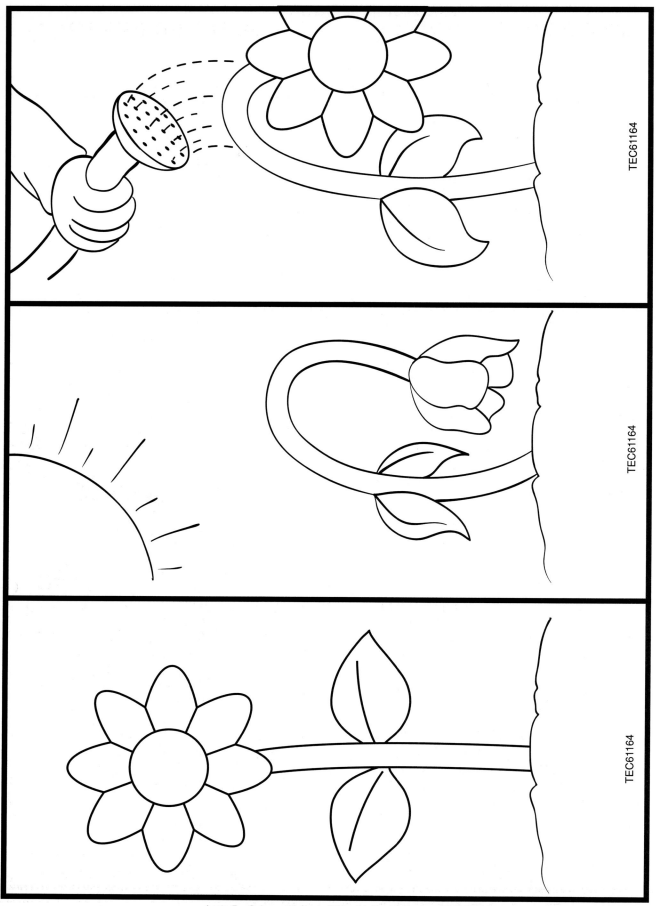

Let's Do Science Today! • ©The Mailbox® Books • TEC61164

Note to the teacher: Have students color and cut out each picture, sequence the pictures from the wilted flower to the healthy flower, and then glue them to a sheet of paper.

A flower needs water.

A tree needs water.

A plant needs water!

What Needs Water?

Name _____

Let's Do Science Today! • ©The Mailbox® Books • TEC61164

Fold-and-Go Booklet: To make a booklet, cut on the bold line. Fold along the thin horizontal line (keeping the programming to the outside) and then fold along the thin vertical line (keeping the cover to the outside). Read aloud each booklet page. Then have each child color the booklet pages and draw rain or water droplets on each page.

Key Science Learning
A plant is made up of several important parts.

During the investigation, students

- make observations
- describe similarities and differences
- identify plant parts
- listen for information
- draw conclusions

Materials:
carrot with a leafy stem,
  placed in a pot with soil
potted flowering plant

Getting Started
Ask students to describe what a plant looks like.

Investigation

STEP 1

Display both the potted carrot and the plant, and have a small group of youngsters describe the similarities and differences between them. Lead students to name each plant's observable parts, encouraging them to use the words *leaf,* *stem,* and *flower.* Then ask, "Do you think there are parts of the plant we cannot see?"

STEP 2

Gently remove the flowering plant from its pot, exposing the roots. Then have students describe them. Tell youngsters we cannot see the roots of most plants because they grow down into the soil to hold the plant in place and to absorb water and minerals.

STEP 3

Gently pull the carrot from the soil and have students identify this familiar vegetable. Explain that a carrot is a plant with an orange root that people eat both raw and cooked.

STEP 4

Have youngsters study the carrot root and then compare it to the roots of the flowering plant.

STEP 5

YUCK!

Ask, "If the carrot has a root that can be eaten, can you eat the roots of the flowering plant?" Lead students to understand that some roots are all right to eat, but others are not.

STEP 6

Hold up the flowering plant and review its parts with students. Then help each child complete a copy of page 44.

Did You Know?

The world's largest carrot weighed 18.99 pounds. Now that's one big carrot!

What Now?

Bring in several other vegetable roots that can be eaten, such as beets, radishes, and sweet potatoes. Have children examine, describe, and compare them. Then prepare the vegetables and invite each child to taste them raw and cooked.

More About
Plant Parts

A Strong, Healthy Plant
Identifying the parts of a plant

Lead youngsters in singing this song to reinforce their understanding of the basic parts of a plant.

(sung to the tune of "The Itsy-Bitsy Spider")

A strong, healthy plant
Has important parts, you know:
Roots, stems, and leaves
That help the plant to grow.
The roots drink the water
And send it up the stem
So the leaves can make the food
And it starts over again.

A "Tree-mendous" Stem!
Comparing

This activity will help students recognize that trees have parts that are comparable to those of smaller plants. Take youngsters on a tree-finding walk. Have them examine the base of the trunk. Point out roots that lead from the trunk down into the ground. Explain that the trunk, branches, and twigs of the tree are all stems, and that water moves from the roots up the trunk of the tree to the leaves, just like it does in a smaller plant.

Note to the teacher: Use with "Plant Parts" on pages 40–42. Have students cut apart the sections and glue them in order on a sheet of paper to complete the plant.

Circle one.

A flowering plant has…

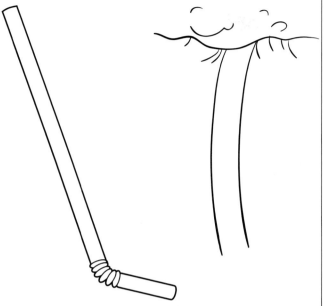

Circle one.

A flowering plant has…

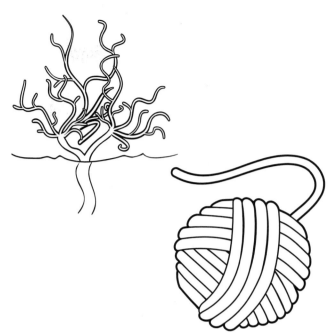

A flowering plant has…

Circle one.

Parts of a
Flowering Plant

Name _____

Let's Do Science Today! • ©The Mailbox® Books • TEC61164

Fold-and-Go Booklet: To make a booklet, cut on the bold line. Fold along the thin horizontal line (keeping the programming to the outside) and then fold along the thin vertical line (keeping the cover to the outside). Read aloud each booklet page and have each child follow the directions to complete her booklet.

45

Marvelous Mud
(Pages 46–51)

Key Science Learning
Mud is formed when soil is mixed with water.

During the investigation, students

- make observations
- make comparisons
- record findings

Materials:
pan of soil
pan of gravel
watering can with water
jumbo craft sticks
chart (see page 47)
marker
recording sheet for each
   child (page 50)
crayons

Getting Started
Ask students to describe experiences with mud.

STEP 1

Gather students and have them predict which mixture will make mud: water and rocks or water and soil. Record youngsters' predictions on a simple chart.

STEP 2

Help a youngster add water to the pan of gravel. Encourage students to watch the rocks closely to see if there are any changes.

STEP 3

Have a child use a craft stick to stir the rocks and water. Ask, "Did the rocks and water make mud?"

STEP 4

Next, help a child add water to the pan of soil. Encourage the students to watch the soil closely to see if there are any changes.

STEP 5

Have a child use a craft stick to stir the soil and water. Ask, "Did the soil and water make mud?"

STEP 6

Give each child a copy of the recording sheet. Encourage each youngster to color the mixture that made mud.

Did You Know?

Some birds, such as flamingos, make their nests out of mud! A flamingo uses its beak to scoop mud into a mound. Then it lays one egg in a hollow at the top of the mound.

What Now?

Place the pan of mud in a sunny area of the classroom and allow it to dry. Have students observe the mud, leading them to notice the change in color and texture as it dries.

More About Mud

Muddy Fun

Fine-motor skills

Place a supply of mud in your sand table or a plastic tub. Provide access to plastic smocks along with small plastic shovels, cookie cutters, measuring cups, and plastic containers. Youngsters visit the center and explore the mud with the provided objects. Now that's a fun fine-motor workout!

What's Growing?

Investigating living things

Give each youngster a cup of soil and have her pour water into it. Invite her to use a craft stick to stir the mixture to make mud. Next, have her sprinkle some grass seed in the mud and then stir the mixture again. Prompt her to place the cup in a sunny area. Then have the student observe the mud each day. No doubt she will be surprised when grass grows from the mud. Explain that the mud provides the soil and water that plants need to live.

Making Mud

🖍 Color.

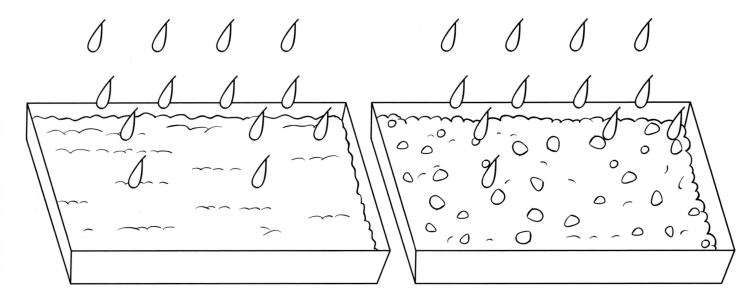

- -

Making Mud

🖍 Color.

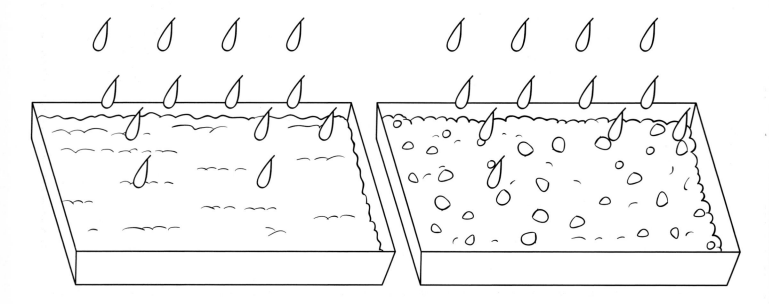

Note to the teacher: Use with "Marvelous Mud" on pages 46–48.

Rain.

Dirt.

Mud!

Mud!

Name _____

Let's Do Science Today! • ©The Mailbox® Books • TEC61164

Fold-and-Go Booklet: To make a booklet, cut on the bold line. Fold along the thin horizontal line (keeping the programming to the outside) and then fold along the thin vertical line (keeping the cover to the outside). Read aloud each booklet page.

51

Key Science Learning
Water can be a solid or a liquid.

During the investigation, students

- make predictions
- use their senses to gather information
- make observations
- communicate ideas
- make comparisons
- discuss cause and effect

Materials:
2 small disposable cups
2 small waterproof toys
2 trays
salt
water

Getting Started
Place a toy in each cup, fill the cups with water, and place the cups in a freezer overnight.

Investigation
Freeze and Melt

STEP 1

Gather a small group of students at a table. Have each child feel the contents of the cups. Say, "Tell me about this cup of water." Lead students to conclude that when water freezes, it changes from a liquid to a solid.

STEP 2

Invite students to examine the ice in each cup. Ask, "What happened to the toys that were placed inside each cup?" Lead youngsters to conclude that the toys are frozen within the ice.

STEP 3

Ask, "What do you think will happen to the ice if it is left out of the freezer?" Lead students to conclude that the ice will melt over time. Then encourage students to brainstorm ways to melt the ice more quickly to free the toys.

STEP 4

Remove the ice from both cups and place each piece on a separate tray. Help students identify the substance in the shaker; then ask, "What do you think would happen if we sprinkled salt onto the ice?"

Investigation
Freeze and Melt

STEP 5

"This one's melting faster!"

Invite students, in turn, to shake salt on one piece of ice, leaving the remaining ice unsalted. Have youngsters observe both pieces of ice and describe what they see happening.

STEP 6

Have students add more salt to the ice as they watch it melt. Remind youngsters that the water was a solid and now it's turning back into a liquid.

This Is Why

Pure water freezes at 32 degrees Fahrenheit. Salt lowers the temperature at which water freezes, causing the ice to melt. This is why road crews use salt to melt ice and make the roads less slippery.

What Now?

Have students watch as you fill a small, empty container with water until the water is about one-quarter of an inch from the top. Mark the outside of the container with a water line and place it in the freezer overnight. Have students examine the container the following day, leading them to notice that as the water froze, it expanded in size!

More About
Freezing and Melting

Juicy Pops
Exploring freezing and melting

Reinforce how a liquid turns into a solid with this yummy idea! Help each child fill a disposable cup about halfway with juice. Have him cover the top of the cup with aluminum foil and then push a craft stick through the foil into the cup. Then just freeze and serve!

For some added fun, help each child make an icepop puppet by following the directions on page 56. Then lead youngsters in showing each face at the appropriate time while reciting the chant shown.

Put a liquid in the freezer
And it turns to ice!
Leave it in the warm air;
It won't look as nice!

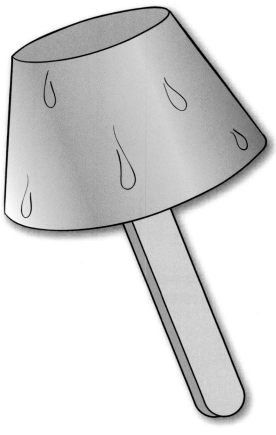

Freeze Pass
Following directions

Students see and feel how a solid turns back into a liquid with this chilly idea! Play some upbeat music and have youngsters pass an ice cube around the circle. Periodically pause the music and have the child with the ice cube hold it up for all to see. Continue in the same manner until the ice cube completely melts away!

TEC61164

TEC61164

TEC61164

TEC61164

Note to the teacher: Use with "Juicy Pops" on page 55. To make a puppet, copy and cut out a puppet pattern. Fold the cutout along the middle line and then glue a craft stick between the puppet halves.

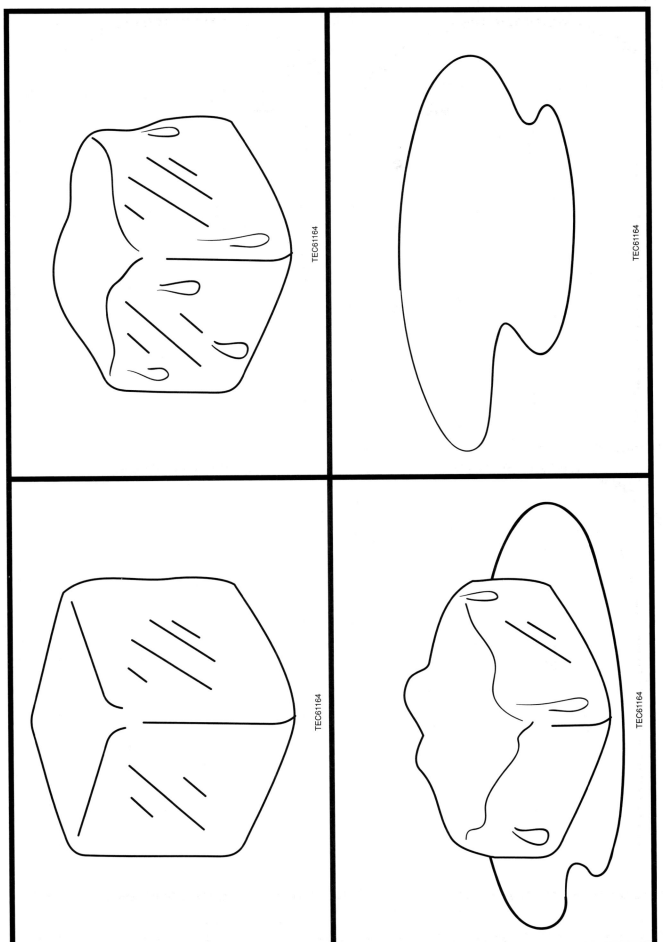

TEC61164

TEC61164

TEC61164

TEC61164

Let's Do Science Today! • ©The Mailbox® Books • TEC61164

Note to the teacher: Copy, cut out, and laminate the cards. Have students arrange the cards in the proper sequence to show the ice cube melting.

57

Key Science Learning

Water is not always a liquid.

During the investigation, students

- make observations
- use their senses to gather information
- make predictions
- discuss and draw conclusions

Materials:
2 plastic jars with lids
pitcher of cold water
ice cubes
food coloring

Getting Started
Ask children how they use water.

Investigation
Water in the Air

Invite a small group of youngsters to join you at a table. Have the students name places water can be found.

Tell students they are going to investigate water. Have each child feel the outside of both plastic jars and verify that they are dry.

STEP 3

Fill one jar with ice cubes. Add cold water to cover the cubes and then fasten the jar lid.

STEP 4

Have students observe the jar of ice and water. As water appears on the outside surface of the jar, invite students to touch it. Ask, "Where did this water come from?"

STEP 5

To confirm that the jar does not have a leak, use the empty jar to repeat Step 3. This time add food coloring to the water. Ask students to predict what will happen.

STEP 6

When water forms on the outside of the second jar, have students touch it. Ask, "Is this water the same color as the water inside the jar? What does this show us?"

This Is Why

Most air contains water vapor. As the surface of the jar cools, the air (and water vapor) around it also cools. Because the cooler air cannot hold as much water vapor, water droplets form and can be seen on the surface of the jar.

What Now?

Ask student where else they have seen water appear. Possible answers include car or kitchen windows, drinking glasses, eyeglasses, and lawns. Help little ones use their new knowledge to explain why the water appeared.

Something to Sing About

Singing a song

When students sing this song, they're reminded that even when they can't see water, it's probably close by.

(sung to the tune of "Frère Jacques")

There is water, there is water
In the air, in the air.
Sometimes you can see it.
Sometimes you cannot, and
I know why, I know why.

Water hides, water hides
In the air, in the air.
This is water's secret.
This is water's secret.
Shhhh, don't tell! Shhhh, don't tell!

Julee said, "The very best thing about water is it takes sticky stuff off my hands."

Keifer said, "The very best thing about water is it cools me off when I am hot like fire."

The Very Best Thing

Sharing an opinion

Turn your students' thoughts about water into an engaging class booklet. Working with one child at a time, write each youngster's dictation as she explains the very best thing about water. Have each child illustrate her work. Then publish the pages in a booklet titled "What We Like About Water."

Name_____

What Likes Water?

Color.

Note to the teacher: Ask the child to name each animal on the page that he thinks likes water and tell why. Then have him color each animal he named.

Water is...

Water is... [inverted]

Water is... [inverted]

Where Is Water?

Name _____

Let's Do Science Today! • ©The Mailbox® Books • TEC61164

Fold-and-Go Booklet: To make a booklet, cut on the bold line. Fold along the thin horizontal line (keeping the programming to the outside) and then fold along the thin vertical line (keeping the cover to the outside). For each booklet page, invite the child to name one or more places water could be.

Key Science Learning
Some objects float; other objects sink.

During the investigation, students

- identify objects and their properties
- make observations
- make predictions
- draw conclusions
- sort and classify

Materials:
plastic tub with water
2 containers, 1 labeled "sink"
   and the other labeled
   "float"
objects that sink and float
copy of page 68 for each child

Getting Started
Help students observe floating and sinking objects.

Investigation
Sink or Float?

STEP 1

Invite a small group of students to join you at a table. Display the items and have students identify them.

STEP 2

"The rock feels heavy!"

Have students examine the items. Encourage youngsters to describe the properties of each item, such as its size, shape, and weight and the type of material it is made from.

STEP 3

Ask, "What does it mean if an object floats?" Lead students to conclude that an object floats if it stays on top of the water. Then ask, "What does it mean if an object sinks?" Help students understand that an object sinks if it drops to the bottom of the water.

STEP 4

"This will Float!"

Sink   Float

Display the tub of water and the sorting containers. Then give each child a copy of the recording sheet on page 68. Have students choose an item and predict if the item will sink or float.

Investigation
Sink or Float?

Invite a child to place the item in the water. Then have students observe whether the object sinks or floats and revisit their predictions. Ask each student to consider why the item sank or stayed afloat and then share his opinion.

Encourage each child to draw a picture of the item on his recording sheet. Then instruct the volunteer to remove the item from the water and place it in the corresponding container. Continue in the same manner with the remaining items.

This Is Why

Water exerts a force that pushes up on objects, the same way gravity pulls them down. An object will float if water pushes up against it hard enough to keep it from sinking. If the object pushes down harder than the water pushes up, the object will sink.

What Now?

Place a golf ball–size piece of clay in a container of water and watch it sink. Next, flatten out the clay and round up the sides so it resembles a boat. Then place the clay boat in the water and observe what happens. Explain that the amount of space an object takes up affects how much water can push up on it, causing the object to either sink or float.

Will It Float?

Singing a song

Have students sing this adorable song before testing several items in a tub of water to see if they float or sink.

(sung to the tune of "When the Saints Go Marching In")

Oh, will it float or will it sink?
Which will it be; what do you think?
Will it stay on top of the water?
Or, like an anchor, will it sink?

Bubbly Bottle

Developing observation skills

Little ones learn how air keeps objects afloat with this idea! Place a cap on an empty bottle. Then invite a student to push the bottle into a bucket of water, top first. Have her let go of the bottle and observe it as it pops back up to the surface. Remove the cap and have her push the bottle into the water as she did before. Then prompt her to tilt the bottle, directing her attention to the bubbles. Explain that bubbles result from the water rushing into the bottle and forcing the air out. When the bottle is full of water, have her let go of it and watch it sink!

Does It Sink or Float?

Let's Do Science Today! • ©The Mailbox® Books • TEC61164

Note to the teacher: Use with "Sink or Float?" on page 64–66.

A ball…

A rock…

A key…

Does It Sink or Float?

Name _____

Fold-and-Go Booklet: To make a booklet, cut on the bold line. Fold along the thin horizontal line (keeping the programming to the outside) and then fold along the thin vertical line (keeping the cover to the outside). Read aloud each booklet page and have students circle the correct picture.

Key Science Learning
Objects can be measured by weight.

During the investigation, students

- make observations
- make predictions
- use senses to gather information
- make comparisons

Materials:
balance
wooden block
large rock, similar in size to the block
cotton batting, similar in size to the block

Getting Started
Have students name items that are light and items that are heavy.

Investigation
Light or Heavy?

STEP 1

Gather a group of youngsters and present the wooden block and the cotton batting. Have each child hold the block and cotton batting. Then prompt him to compare the weight of the two objects using words such as *heavier* and *lighter*.

STEP 2

Have a child place the block on one side of the balance and the cotton batting on the other side. Explain that the heavier item will tip the balance downward. Lead youngsters to conclude that the block is heavier.

STEP 3

Once again, have each child hold the block. Then encourage him to search the classroom to find another object that is lighter than the block, just like the cotton batting is.

STEP 4

Next, have each child hold the wooden block and the rock. Prompt him to compare the weight of the two objects using the words *heavier* and *lighter*.

STEP 5

Have a child place the rock on one side of the balance and the block on the other side. Encourage students to watch the balance. Then lead them to conclude that the rock is heavier than the block.

STEP 6

Give students another opportunity to hold the block. Then prompt each youngster to search the classroom to find another object that is heavier than the block, just like the rock is.

Did You Know?

The heaviest animal on Earth is the blue whale, weighing more than 300,000 pounds. It's heavier than 25 elephants or 115 giraffes!

What Now?

Place a variety of common classroom objects at a center along with the balance. Invite youngsters to visit the center and place items on the balance to compare the items' weights.

More About Weight

Light as a Feather

Reciting a poem

Have youngsters recite this fun poem with great dramatic flair. For extra fun, prompt them to recite all the lines that discuss light objects with high whispery voices and all the lines discussing heavy objects with deep loud voices.

Light as a feather, light as a bee,
Light as a butterfly, light as a key.
Heavy as an elephant, heavy as a train,
Heavy as a dinosaur, heavy as a plane.
Everything has a weight, you see.
Heavy as a dump truck, light as a flea.

A Weighty Comparison

Comparing weights

Make copies of pages 74 and 75 for each child. Remind each youngster that heavy objects will cause a balance to tip downward. Then help her draw a picture of a heavy item on the left side of the balance on page 74 and a light item on the right side. Next, have her color and cut out the cards on page 75. Encourage her to sort the cards into piles of heavy objects and light objects. Stack the cards that show heavy items and staple them to the left side of the balance. Then staple the lighter items to the right side of the balance. The youngster can flip through the items and compare the objects' weights.

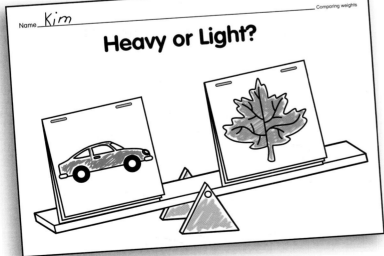

Heavy or Light?

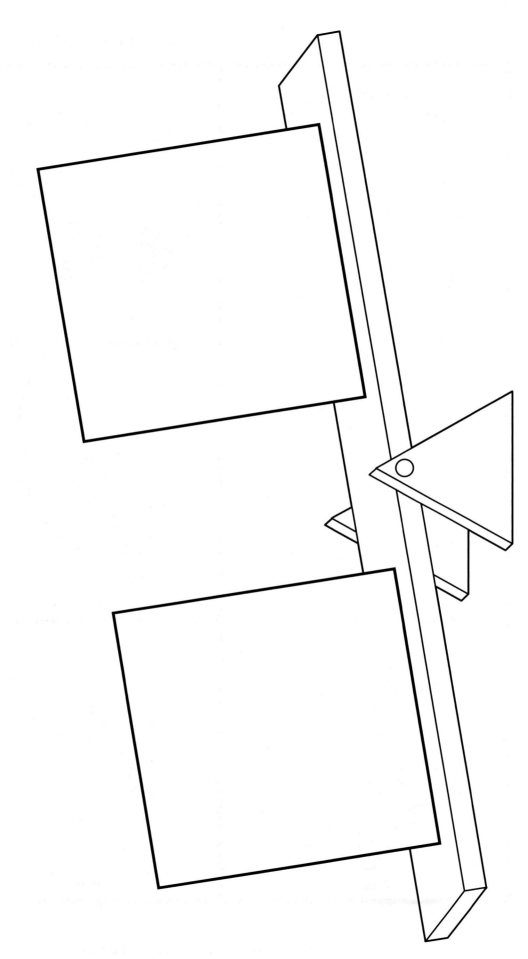

Note to the teacher: Use with "A Weighty Comparison" on page 73.

TEC61164

TEC61164

TEC61164

TEC61164

TEC61164

TEC61164

Key Science Learning
Magnets attract objects that are made of steel.

During the investigation, students

● make observations

● make predictions

● use the senses to gather information

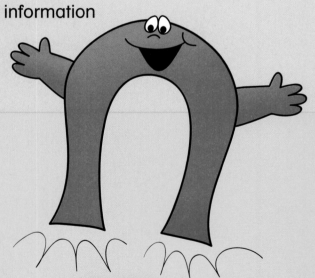

Materials:
large strong magnet for
   each child
jumbo paper clips
index card for each child
box lid
sand

Getting Started
Ask youngsters what
they know about
magnets.

Instant Attraction

STEP 1

Gather students and give each child a magnet and a few jumbo paper clips. Invite children to explore the items and discuss what they observe.

STEP 2

Gather the paper clips. Then ask, "Will an index card stick to the magnet like the paper clips did?" After youngsters discuss their thoughts, give each child an index card and prompt her to place it against her magnet.

STEP 3

Next, have each child place one paper clip on the tabletop and then place the index card over the paper clip. Ask, "What do you think will happen if you touch the magnet to the top of the index card while it's hiding a paper clip?" After students share their predictions, have each youngster see if the paper clip is attracted to the magnet through the index card.

STEP 4

Ask, "How many paper clips do you think the magnet can pick up through the card?" Have students share their guesses. Then encourage youngsters to place several paper clips under their cards and see how many paper clips are attracted to their magnets.

STEP 5

The paper clips are moving!

Place several paper clips in the box lid. Then ask, "Do you think the magnet will attract the paper clips through the lid?" Encourage students to share their thoughts. Then have each child observe the paper clips as she runs her magnet along the bottom of the lid.

STEP 6

It took the paper clips out of the sand.

Cover the paper clips with a shallow layer of sand. Ask, "Do you think a magnet can pick up the paper clips through the sand?" After students share their predictions, have a student pass her magnet over the top of the sand and encourage students to describe what they see. Then lead youngsters to understand that a magnet attracts paper clips because these paper clips contain steel, and magnets attract steel.

This Is Why

Objects containing iron, steel, nickel, and cobalt are attracted by magnets. Magnetic force can act through a variety of materials, such as paper and sand, depending on the strength of the magnet.

What Now?

Stock a center with magnets in a variety of sizes and strengths. Also place at the center objects that magnets will attract as well as objects that magnets will not attract. Invite students to explore the objects and decide which items are attracted by the magnets and which are not.

More About Magnets

Opposites Attract
Investigating magnetism

Hang a bar magnet from a tabletop as shown. Then place a loose bar magnet in the center. A youngster picks up the loose magnet and places one of the ends against the hanging magnet. Through exploration, the youngster will notice that when certain ends (north and south) are placed together, they are attracted to each other. When other ends (north and north or south and south) are placed together, the magnets repel each other.

Attraction Art
Using a science concept to create art

Tape a piece of construction paper to a cookie sheet. Dip jumbo washers in different colors of tempera paint and then place them on the paper. A youngster slides a magnet over the bottom of the cookie sheet, moving the washers over the paper. Add more paint-covered washers as desired. When the youngster is satisfied with his painting, he removes the washers and sets the artwork aside to dry.

Paper Clip Pickup

My magnet:

How many paper clips?

Note to the teacher: Have each child trace a magnet in the space provided. Then encourage her to dip the magnet into a container of jumbo paper clips. Have her remove the paper clips attached to the magnet, count them, and then write the number (with help as needed) in the space provided. Have her repeat the process with other magnets and copies of this page.